Spirituality is the heart and soul of yoga. Regardless of what system of yoga you practice, the underlying core intention is to lead you to the final experience of Samadhi—the union of Shiva and Shakti.

Philosophical teachings on unity consciousness found in spiritual, theological or yoga books are merely conceptual. Without direct experience, words are like paper flowers, appealing to the eye but without fragrance or life.

Amrit Yoga guides you from the philosophy of unity to the direct experience of unity of body, mind, heart and soul. It is meditation in motion, transforming the philosophy of yoga into experiential reality.

Amrit Yoga and The Posture of Consciousness are registered trademarks.

Table of Contents

Experiencing the Power of Yoga
The Science of Alchemy and Union

The depth of the integrative experience of yoga comes not from force or flexibility of the body, but from meditative awareness. The secret of yoga, the science of alchemy (moving from conflicting duality to unity consciousness), cannot be delivered through philosophy. Words of wisdom are like a map that must be traveled to awaken the power that lies within you. Words may express the power of transformation but have no power to transmit the experience of transformation. No matter how bright the light of a painted candle, it cannot illumine the darkness. To transmit the light of unity consciousness, one must have the facility to enter the depth of unity where the darkness of duality dissolves into the direct experience of light, love and unity.

To communicate unity, the teacher must establish a communion level channel of direct energetic transmission of the sacred experience of divine union. Yogi Desai has been blessed by his Kundalini Master, H.H. Swami Kripalvanandji, to transmit this experience directly to sincere yoga students. In yoga, this is known as *shaktipat.* Thousands have experienced the power of *shakti* embodied by Yogi Desai. It radiates through his presence and emanates through his teaching, chanting, guided meditations and his demonstration of meditation in motion. It creates a powerful synergistic impact transmitted by osmosis to all those who are receptive and open. Shakti carries within it the power to awaken deeper levels of integrative awareness. The insight and awakening he initiates can work miracles in your personal, family and business life. The focus of Yogi Desai's teaching is to empower you to access the infinite source of consciousness (Shiva) and divine energy (Prana Shakti) inborn within you.

Yogi Desai's in-depth study and insights combined with his direct experience of awakening makes his teaching a powerful transmission. He has a unique facility to translate ancient secrets and words of wisdom into terminology that is easy to adopt in the practice of yoga and in a Western lifestyle.

Yogi Desai introduces authentic principles, techniques and tools to help even a novice student enter the deepest levels of relaxation, tranquility and stillness. Meditation in motion creates a direct link to the integrative power of yoga. When Yogi Desai enters the state of deep stillness, the spiritual force field spreads rapidly and fills the entire room. The combined power of ancient wisdom infused with divine energy and consciousness creates an opening for those who are seeking a quantum leap in their spiritual growth.

Lila Ivey

Editor

The Birth of Amrit Yoga

by Yogi Amrit Desai

In 1970, I had an extraordinary experience that revealed to me a whole new dimension in the practice of yoga. One morning, while I was performing yoga postures, as I had done for many years, my body spontaneously entered a flow of automatic movements that were guided from within. These movements were accompanied by a state of ecstatic meditation deeper than anything I had ever experienced before. My movements were effortless and deeply engaging. They were prompted directly from bodily urges; my mind took a back seat. My body became extremely limber. The postures were emerging directly from bodily impulses unsolicited by my prior training in conventional postures. I was in awe of the new flexibility that came to me without struggle or force. My movements were no longer connected to my pre-programmed ego-mind and self-image.

For the first time, I felt complete and total integration of body, mind, heart and spirit. All internal conflicts, doubts and impatience disappeared. It was an experience of meditation in motion. The movements were directly flowing from the primal wisdom of prana (Prana Shakti) and consciousness (Shiva).

It was truly the divine dance of Shiva and Shakti performed in the field of my body that drew me into the deepest levels of ecstasy and union. I was no longer "performing" the postures. The duality and separation of performer and performance—actor and act—dancer and dance—disappeared. I was so absorbed in the experience I lost all sense of time. I was completely engrossed in the timeless experience of the present moment. I had entered a state of deep stillness in the midst of motion. This was an orgasmic experience of sacred union—of Shiva and Shakti.

Before this, I had practiced yoga for 20 years and was an experienced Hatha Yoga instructor. Even though I was extremely flexible and performed postures with great ease and understanding of the core principles of yoga, I had never entered such depth of unity. The true meaning of yoga was revealed to me experientially.

After this phenomenal gift appeared for me, I wrote to my guru, Swami Kripalvanandji, one of the most prominent Kundalini masters in India. He informed me that my experience was a manifestation of the awakening of prana, the stage prior to the awakening of kundalini. On a rudimentary level, prana carries out all life-sustaining survival level involuntary functions. On a higher level, this awakened prana generates all evolutionary functions automatically. The same intelligence that carries out all life-giving functions now accelerates to an evolutionary level. Awakened prana generates postures, pranayamas, cleansing kriyas, locks and mudras, removing blockages from the entire chakra system. This leads the shakti from lower centers of consciousness to unite with the highest center, the thousand-petaled lotus. When a yogi reaches this highest stage, it is called *Samadhi*. Awakened prana helps us encounter the layers of unconscious fears and emotional stress that are holding us back, preventing us from exploring our inborn divine potential.

To my amazement and delight, this experience recurred for me day after day. Even though I had enjoyed my yoga practice before my spontaneous flow experience, I fell in love with my practice even more because I was progressively entering into deeper and deeper states of my being. As my mind was drawn inward, my awareness was disengaged from the external surroundings. I was no longer the performer—the postures were being performed through me. It was as if "I" had disappeared and had become the postures themselves. I had merged into my performance.

The yoga I was now practicing took me to an expanded state of consciousness and permanently changed my life. I was able to explore, expand and experience new levels of yoga as I continued my practice. When I returned to my daily activities after practice, I returned with greater awareness. The impact of this practice extended into the way I encountered the challenges of my life. I was able to maintain my inner balance in the midst of daily interactions. I found myself coming from a new level of spontaneity and relaxation, rather than acting from unconscious habitual behavior.

Soon after this life-transforming experience, I began to conceive of an innovative new approach to the practice of yoga, where movement and meditation, Hatha and Raja Yoga, can occur simultaneously and complement one another. All of my previous concepts about yoga dropped away. I had believed that the study of yoga and hard work would lead to deeper meditative levels. All that changed with the realization that was revealed to me that morning.

It is the integration of the principles of awakened prana and meditative awareness that distinguish Amrit Yoga. It is the yoga of direct experience—the dance of Shiva and Shakti—consciousness and energy—entwined in the divine ecstasy of union.

Amrit Yoga — The Posture of Consciousness™

Amrit Yoga is not confined to the physical posture. It is a system in which physical postures are used as a vehicle to reconnect with the integrative source within. When you bring mindful meditative attention to the practice of Hatha Yoga postures, you not only address physical limitations, you also work through your psychic inhibitions, creating an opening for the integrative process to actualize in your life. As a result, what you think, what you say, and what you do are in complete alignment at all times. Then your practice of yoga and your life are holistically moving in harmony with each other.

By linking meditative awareness to the physical posture, it becomes the posture of consciousness. Connecting the physical posture with meditative awareness naturally allows you to relax your into your body. Adding conscious breathing helps you disengage from contracting muscles and defensive tensions and increases your range of motion without struggle or force. The period that follows the actual performance of the posture is the second half of the posture. The posture of consciousness does not stop with the completion of the physical posture. It extends into the transition time. No matter how brief the interval, no matter how short the transition time, anchor your undivided total attention to fully feel the flood of energy released by the posture. Feel the presence of the released energy in the form of sensations in your body. After feeling the sensations fully in your body, draw your attention to the Third Eye.

The Integrative Center of the Third Eye

All the energy that has been released from the tensions in your emotional or physical blocks will be carried instantly by your attention to the Third Eye. It is in Third Eye that the energies of the shadow self and psychic blocks are transformed through an integrative process that converts darkness into light and duality into unity. The Third Eye is the integrative center where dualities lose their conflicting forces and become integrated, harmonious and whole.

The transitions or spaces between each asana are just as important as the formal postures themselves. In releasing the posture, remain attentive to every movement and bodily sensation. Every time you finish the posture allow yourself to enter the celebration of deep release. Being engaged in the sensations of the released energy is the most absorbing experience of the mind naturally merging and melting into the energy body.

There are two levels of integration:
   – *the first level is the release of blocked psychosomatic energies;*
   – *the second level is integration of the released energies through the Third Eye.*

Most yoga practices only engage themselves in the release of energy. Guiding the released energy to its integrative state in the Third Eye is seldom recognized. As a result, a crucial, integrative experience of yoga is not fully encompassed.

The integrative process that begins by releasing stress- and fear-bound energies into the body during the yoga posture continues to move toward deeper integration during the interim period when you may think you have already finished the posture. Keep your attention deeply engaged in the sensations that are felt in the body not only during the postures but also after the release of the posture. During the posture you are unblocking the unconscious psychosomatic forces and during the transition time you are integrating those forces by transforming them from darkness to light.

Prana Mimics the Mind

This merging of the mental and energy bodies takes place when the mind is no longer the carrier of its unconscious programming. The prana body follows the conscious and unconscious activities of the mental or emotional body. When the mental or emotional body is in confusion, hesitation, doubt or impatience it is instantly reflected as inhibition in the prana body. This prevents prana from freely carrying out all the life-giving, healing and regenerative processes.

Our pranic energy is held hostage by compulsive, unconscious forces that will not easily release it. To disengage prana from unconscious forces, Amrit Yoga uses the powerful spiritual tool of inward focus and meditative awareness to systematically reconnect with the source.

When the mental and emotional bodies deeply integrate into the energy body, all of the distractions that are ordinarily present in the waking state disappear. Each time your mind releases its control over prana, prana energy acts with greater strength and freedom to carry out internal healing at a much higher and accelerated rate. This is the process of freeing prana from the unconscious forces that actively work through the medium of the mental and emotional bodies. This is the meaning of surrendering our will to prana. Once you learn how to surrender to sensations, you will be able to enter the deeper level experience of ecstasy and unity of yoga.

Remember: The first part of the posture that you are actively, willfully performing releases the blocked energies and the second part that follows is entry into a state of non-doing where you are just simply allowing undivided attention to be totally engaged in receiving the full impact of the released energy as it is felt in the form of sensations.

Healing Prana Goes Where it is Needed

When prana is disengaged from the psychosomatic blocks during postures, the released energy is no longer contaminated or charged by the personalized,

18

preprogrammed conditionings of our self-concepts. This energy that is disengaged from the self-concepts assumes the original primal purity of universal intelligence. This pure energy perceives clearly without personal distortions and is then available to be used deliberately and willfully for surrender. When our energy body is purified we can naturally live in the beginner's mind. The more energy we transform from unconscious psychosomatic blocks to the Third Eye the more we become self-sourcing, self-confident, creative, intuitive, insightful and objective in our perceptions and directions in life.

During the postures, if your attention is scattered and disturbed by your personal preprogrammed patterns of mental and emotional reactions, then your energy remains engaged in old karmic patterns. Erasing these karmic patterns is the real work of yoga; letting go of the conditioned past that lives in the unconscious. This integrative process continues throughout the entire practice of Amrit Yoga in either the performance of the posture, holding the posture or in the transition in between. For this integrative process to be complete, you must remain in mindful, meditative awareness to all the subtle sensations that accompany each and every movement.

19

Staying in the feeling center requires acute vigilance to recognize any mental or emotional interference that draws away your attention. In order to keep the internal focus total and undivided, you must remain in your feeling center without being caught by personal biases and conditioned reactions.

For you to enter this level of deep integration you must remain inwardly focused, deeply feeling the energy flowing and flooding in different areas of your body. You're simply observing the impact of the movements, stretches, holding and releasing of the posture. Every time you come out of the posture, use inward focus to observe the impact of released energies. This energy invariably follows your attention and also increases the impact of the released energies. If you miss it, no matter how well you have performed the first part, you have gone only half way.

Remaining in the Witness

When you remain in this non-participative, choiceless witness you will be able to disengage from mental and emotional distortions that disturb your ability to live totally and fully in your bodily sensations. The more you remain witness to your sensations the more you will find that the prana body will be released from the distorting influences of the mental and emotional bodies. This is the process of purifying your prana body. As a result, you will find the contaminations that are imparted by the mental and emotional bodies into the prana body are progressively separated. This process of returning is what Christ meant when he said, "Unless ye be like children again, ye cannot enter the kingdom of heaven." In Buddhism the same state of consciousness is expressed by the term "beginner's mind." Again, remaining witness to the internal workings of prana automatically allows your released prana to feed your higher Self rather then your emotional or mental bodies.

All of our pre-programmed beliefs, personal biases, attractions and repulsions, addictions and fears, form the body of our self-image that we also know as our persona or mask. In order to maintain, nurture and protect this mask from being exposed, our unconscious, survival instinct engages the life force of prana to support and sustain that self-image. This is how the distorting influences of the self-image weaken the healing power of prana. When the self-image protects itself, it draws on the life force of prana. As a result, prana is unable to fulfill its innate evolutionary process to lead us toward the higher centers of consciousness.

The entire process of the practice of Amrit Yoga is designed to free the prana body by disassociating it from the unconscious, preprogrammed self-image, personal biases and belief systems that prevent the healing power of prana from serving as an evolutionary agent of the higher Self.

The Power of Intention

The meaning of the word yoga is union. The purpose of the practice of yoga is to experience unity of body, mind, heart and soul.

All human suffering is the direct result of stress caused by internal conflicts. These conflicts drain our vital life force and are the root of our misery. All day long, regardless of where we are or what we are doing, these unconscious fears, frustrations, blame and shame produce internal mental dialogues and images. These constant mental disruptions keep us from being relaxed, creative and effective.

The practice of Amrit Yoga provides specific guidelines, principles, tools and techniques to harness the scattered forces of attention. When you enter the field of harmonious unity, where all of you is acting as a whole, you are in the "posture of integrative consciousness."

The central focus in the practice of yoga is "intention."

You must have *in the beginning* what you want *in the end.* If you want mangoes, you must first plant a mango seed. When it is nurtured with fertilizer, water, sunshine and care, it eventually becomes a tree that bears fruit. Its potential becomes actualized.

If yoga is to fulfill its meaning—the merging of individual-separative consciousness into cosmic consciousness—your practice must be impregnated with intention as the seed of integration. This intention is like a mission statement that guides and structures every stage of the practice of Amrit Yoga.

In the beginning stage, the intention is planted as a potential seed. The intention becomes a constant reference to infuse your practice with the seed of integrative awareness. As you integrate the core principles, techniques and tools that focus your attention, the seed begins to grow. You progressively enter a deeper, more integrated state, leading toward the actualization of your intention.

Physical yoga postures are used as an entry point to the true practice of yoga. Amrit Yoga uses Hatha Yoga postures as a foundation to bring about *nadi shuddhi—*

the purification of the body's nerve channels, balancing the function of glands and ridding the body of toxins. This simultaneously retards the aging process and increases vitality, endurance and flexibility.

To confine the profound depth of yoga and to use it exclusively as a body-centered practice is like clipping the wings of an airplane and using it as an automobile. The purpose of Amrit Yoga is to give wings to your practice to explore, expand and experience the infinite power of spirit that you are.

Over time, those of you who have consistently practiced various forms of Hatha Yoga will have built the groundwork that allows you to extend your practice into a new dimension. This added spiritual depth enhances not only your practice on the yoga mat, but also gives you new courage to face the challenges you encounter in life—painful transition periods, relationships and crises—as an opening for personal transformation.

Amrit Yoga is designed to transform the philosophy of yoga into an experiential reality.

Without integration, there is no yoga. The focus in yoga is on integration of the body, mind and spirit. The aim is to consciously bring these separate forces into balance, harmony and unity.

Body-centered practices, such as the way Hatha Yoga is usually practiced, is the basis for exploring deeper levels of integration, and yet, in this new approach, the demand for flexibility or strength is not a primary requirement. While it is necessary to practice postures with correct form and proper precision, perfecting the posture is not the goal. Experiencing the union of yoga remains the focus.

The techniques used in Amrit Yoga are focused on developing meditative consciousness.

Amrit Yoga is a unique blend of yoga postures, breath control, concentration and meditation, all practiced simultaneously as meditation in motion. The emphasis is on awakening the body's natural wisdom to unleash the healing power of prana shakti. When the conflicting forces of body, mind and spirit are harnessed and harmonized, you enter an ecstatic experience that is deeply absorbing, relaxing and fulfilling.

Using the techniques practiced in Amrit Yoga, you are progressively releasing deeper layers of stress held in the subtle bodies. This extends the healing power of yoga, elevating the popular concept of Hatha Yoga as a physical discipline. By releasing the prana that is blocked and trapped on subtler layers, the scope of yoga is enhanced.

When you enter the sacred experience of Amrit Yoga, you are drawn into the deepest relaxation. The whole body throbs with the healing energy of prana. Energy swells and floods through every cell, every nerve and every muscle to all levels of your being. Bathing in the flood of divine energy (Shakti) you enter the timeless zone of grace, beauty and ecstasy. You melt into the infinite ocean of cosmic consciousness and disappear, just as when a drop falls into the water and merges into the oneness of the ocean. The drop becomes infinite. You do not know where you went or how long you stayed until you return to ordinary consciousness. Each time you enter the state of silent ecstasy, it becomes easier and easier to return there and remain longer.

Amrit Yoga is a metaphor for life.

It is practiced both on and off the mat. From the deep stillness and relaxation created by the practice of Amrit Yoga, you will develop consciousness when life places you in a painful psychic posture. Instead of struggling with your spouse or your boss, your new awareness will allow you to carry the lessons of yoga into your daily life.

Yoga is not a physical discipline you practice for an hour a day. Yoga is a way of life you practice all day, every day. The light of consciousness provides you with an opening to the divine potential that is inborn and always present within you.

Breath — A Tool for Transformation

There is a deep relationship between breath, thoughts, emotions and movement. They interact with and affect each other. Breath acts as a link between the physical body, the mental body and the emotional body. In Amrit Yoga, the breath is used as a powerful tool to gather the scattered forces of all of the bodies to function harmoniously in co-creation.

Stress in the body or fear in the mind instantly alters the breath patterns. Changing your breath pattern helps release stress. Breath, combined with consciousness, has an added impact on harmonizing the conflicting unconscious forces that keep you from being relaxed and focused during your yoga practice and in your daily life.

In the practice of yoga, breath is used to eliminate stress not only in the body, but also stress that is continually introduced by mental and emotional reactions. Breath connects the body to the mind and the mind to

the body. Breath is a bridge between the body-mind because it is subtler than the body and grosser than the
mind.

**Changing physical and emotional reactions are
in direct relationship to breathing patterns.**
As you alter your breath to a steady flow, your mind
becomes calm and relaxed. You can refocus your attention on your bodily sensations. When the body and
mind are in co-creation, they spontaneously and automatically support each other. In the absence of conflict
and stress, they function as a team and produce the synergistic power of the spirit.

In your practice, regulated breath will help you cross
your physical, mental and emotional boundaries. It will
take you to a deeper level in a relaxed rather than a
forced way, both in your body and in life situations.
When there is resistance in your body or fear in the
mind, consciously changing your breath pattern will
help release defensive holding patterns. The combined
use of breath and consciousness will invariably help you
break through holding in the physical as well as the
subtle bodies. When you find yourself resisting either
a physical or psychological block, the breath is very ef-

fective in helping release the grip of old reactive patterning. Then you are free to act consciously, deliberately breaking through your fears, self-concepts and personal biases.

Use breath to manage your internal psychic posture as well as your external physical posture. Breath is psychosomatic; it integrates, modifies and orchestrates the body-mind experience. To shift out of reaction to fear or pain, you must deliberately shift out of your protective breathing pattern. It will relieve pain caused by fear and resistance. Changing your breathing patterns is an integral part of the willful practice of yoga. Conscious use of the breath allows you to shift out of old habits and replace them with new awareness.

Pain in the body is held in the muscles and joints; fear in the mind (of being hurt) adds defensive muscle resistance, which is the body in reaction. So when you are performing a yoga posture, you encounter two types of pain:

> – *Pain that is already lodged in the body.*
> – *Pain that is held in unconscious memories of the past that manifest as fear in the mind.*

When you encounter resistance in your body, notice how it shows up in your breath. You may instinctively hold your breath or breathe erratically to cope with the discomfort. This also happens in life situations. When life puts you in an emotionally uncomfortable posture (when you are caught in fear, insecurity, resentment or emotional reaction), your psychic body is placed in a yoga posture. You are facing a psychological boundary whether you are in a physical posture or a psychic posture. Notice how your breath changes to accommodate physical, mental and emotional stress.

Making the shift from a physical posture to a psychic posture.

When you practice a physical posture, it is an external form. Your unconscious reactions caused by fear or pain place your subtle (mental and emotional) bodies into a psychic posture. This means your psychic posture is in conflict with the physical posture. When you consciously breathe, relax and let go, your attention is disengaged from reaction and can be refocused on bodily sensations. Now your body and mind are in harmony.

Psychic postures driven by the unconscious will surface as you perform physical postures. They are often in conflict and not supportive of physical postures. Amrit Yoga provides you with the tools and techniques to enter the posture of consciousness where you have the opportunity to release the psychic block held in your subtle bodies.

Use the psychic posture as a yoga posture and use the breath to relax, to be released from the psychic boundary that holds you back. Along with the powerful tool of breath, you must learn to use the even more powerful tool of meditative awareness to cross the psychosomatic boundaries. The posture of integrative consciousness begins with the psychosomatic and evolves into the bio-spiritual. The ultimate tool that carries you through the invisible boundaries of the physical body, the energy body, the mental body and the emotional body is meditative awareness. Meditative awareness will allow you to release the tight grip of pre-programmed emotional patterns. You will progressively move into deeper and deeper levels of experiential unity and ecstasy born of the orgasmic union of Shiva and Shakti.

In your practice, as you learn to combine the power of breath and consciousness, your mental and emotional disturbances will diminish. In the absence of interference by the ego-mind, your practice becomes the dance of Shiva and Shakti. It will take you deeper and deeper into stillness. These blocks you encounter in your physical and subtle bodies keep your soul shackled to the lower centers of consciousness. When the higher consciousness guides the lower, the lower becomes transformed into higher. When the lower unconscious instinctive ego-self guides the higher consciousness, the higher manifests as lower.

During the holding of the posture you will begin to cross boundaries where you may experience discomfort or pain. As a result, the form of breath—rapid, slow, rhythmic or strained—will change to meet the needs of your body's demands. For example, if you had suffered an injury or a pulled muscle in the past, it is held in your muscle memory. The memory of the hurt will return to protect you from being hurt again. This is a natural process that keeps you from hurting yourself over and over again. Some of the experiences of hurt in the past may have been true at the time. Even though the same hurtful conditions are no longer present, the memory that is bound to the experience will automatically return to protect you. This is unconscious reactivated-action or reaction. The resistance to hurt is built into our survival instinct as fear. When you face the memory of hurt, your muscles will contract and your breath pattern will shift to cope with the fear of pain. It functions unconsciously and acts automatically, independent of your will. At such times, conscious breathing creates a space where you can replace reaction with a deliberate action to work through the memory block.

Who is pushing your buttons?

Using breath and consciousness is the secret to freedom from the captivity of old memories. Past hurts that live as a memory are assets only when used consciously, but when used mechanically, they act as psychic blocks. They prevent you from moving out of the invisible walls that create a "circle of safety" around you. Amrit Yoga uses the combination of breath and meditative awareness as a way to cross unconscious memory boundaries that were formed when you were physically or psychologically abused, betrayed, taken advantage of or rejected. These memories instinctively return to protect you whenever you push your own "memory button." This will happen automatically by performing a posture, entering intimate relationships, engaging in any spiritual discipline or activities such as sports, art or music. All such disciplines are designed to push your memory buttons.

The difference between a spiritual discipline and other forms of discipline is that spiritual practices are adopted with an intention to remain the witness. You must be the witness instead of judging yourself or blaming others for the pain it causes when your karmic buttons are pushed either by you or by others. When you are in the witness state, there is no blame, there is no shame, there is no attraction or repulsion to whatever surfaces. Your focus is on eliminating karma buttons, not the button-pusher.

If you do not adopt spiritual disciplines, such as Hatha Yoga, Raja Yoga, Bhakti Yoga or Karma Yoga, your intimate relationships, family life and business life will create situations where life itself will push your memory buttons.

Life is a perpetual therapeutic irritation.

If you have unresolved memory buttons, you have the option of practicing yoga, where you push your own buttons. The old memories, fears, personal biases, beliefs, insecurities and self-concepts will surface, manifesting as personal attractions and repulsions, addictions and fears. If you choose not to enter a spiritual discipline, life will do it for you anyway. Life is a school for the evolutionary journey of the soul. If you choose to ignore it, life situations will go on, increasing the intensity of pain until you recognize and release your resistance to reality. This is why I say: Life is a perpetual therapeutic irritation.

Ask yourself these questions.

When life situations push my buttons:

1. *How can I use them to eliminate my self-image and self-concepts that prevent me from living fully in the freedom of now?*

2. *When I perceive fear, how can I recognize the difference between the "memory" of fear and "real" fear?*

3. *How do I encounter the person who pushes my buttons? Is he my enemy? Is he my friend?*

4. *When someone pushes my memory button, do I automatically blame the button pusher?*

5. *Do I try to eliminate the button or the button pusher?*

❋

From Conflict to Co-Creative Oneness

Resolution of Conflicting Voices into the Unity of Yoga

The body, mind, heart and ego live in a conflict of interests. When the heart says, "I want love," the ego says "Stay in control," and the mind says, "I want to have more sex." So the body automatically follows the strongest voice and the internal conflict continues. We are not loving, we are practicing conflict in the name of love.

Or...before a meal, the heart says, "Eat moderately." During the meal, the ego says, "Enjoy yourself, have more." After the meal, the mind says, "I hate overeating." Again, we are not eating, we are practicing conflict. Regardless of what we are doing—driving, cooking, working or practicing yoga—the static of internal conflict goes on and on. Even when we think we are practicing yoga, we are practicing conflict.

Within us lives not one but a crowd of voices with conflicting interests. *Witness consciousness* (see page 50)

is the ultimate tool of the spirit that harnesses the conflicting voices and harmonizes their restorative healing power to function optimally. Often, it is not age or illness that depletes us of youthful vitality or robs us of the joy of life, it is the ongoing inner conflict, indecision and self-doubt that undermine everything we do. When one part of us wants to change self-defeating behavior, another part resists or fights back. It is as if our two hands were enemies fighting one another. No matter which one wins, we lose.

Integration is the most potent tool in the practice of yoga. It unites the conflicting voices. Through intention and commitment to consistent practice, witness consciousness brings conflicting polarity into co-creative unity. When we are integrated, we move out of the conflicting forces of the lower three centers of survival, sensation and power, and step into the heart and the higher centers of love and compassion.

That which is stressful and irritating is separative. That which is relaxing and fulfilling is also the most unifying. To make our usual conflicts disappear, we are often attracted to activities we call "entertainment" or "hobbies" because they are the most engaging and unifying. Some people entertain themselves with sex, food, alcohol, work or tranquilizers, while others take up hobbies, such as music, dance, arts or sports to reduce stress, relax and feel good. Regardless of what we use to relax, the underlying force is the experience of integration it generates. We are attracted to the experience that engages us so totally that we feel fulfilled and renewed. This means that while we may not realize it, we are all attracted to the experience of the unity of yoga. Deep within each one of us is the urge to merge. But instead of facing our lives consciously, we deceive ourselves by using temporary measures to enter false unity. In psychology, avoiding the real source of stress is called "escape." When we use entertainment and hobbies as escapes, the level of attachment or addiction we form is directly proportional to the stress it relieves. However, entertainment we use just as entertainment has no addictive power.

Even when we are performing postures on a yoga mat this internal conflict is going on. This is not the practice of yoga because there is no integration of the body, mind, heart and spirit. This is the practice of separative ego that induces subtle conflict on the yoga mat, such as when we:

  – *entertain thoughts of fear, we generate internal dialogues and images that support fear.*

  – *judge our performance or compare it with others (self-rejection).*

  – *are impatient and want to complete a routine so we can go on to the next thing.*

  – *unconsciously resist pain or discomfort and either avoid facing it or aggressively force ourselves to overcome boundaries we encounter in our bodies (fight or flight, unconscious reaction).*

*– get frustrated, angry or jealous when our expecta-
tions of performance are not met.*

When we do something that engages our total attention, we become undivided and whole. With complete
absorption comes deep relaxation and a sense of fulfill-
ment and satisfaction. We lose all sense of time and
space. The dancer disappears into the dance, the musi-
cian disappears into the music. The pleasure we experience in such activities is not the result of what we do,
but how we do it so that it engages us fully and dissolves
all internal conflicts and disturbing thoughts and emotions. Even when we practice yoga postures, if they fail
to engage us totally, it is not the experience of yoga (unity)
when the performer dissolves into the performance.

Amrit Yoga is meditation in motion, where we live
in integrative awareness on the yoga mat and in life.
This consciousness keeps us present, total and undivided, regardless of what we do or where we go.

✤

Merging into the Flow of Sensation

Expanding your Sense-ability to Induce
Deeper Integration

In the next phase of your yoga practice, you learn to
move from your thinking (head) center into your feeling (heart) center. Amrit Yoga is a journey from the
head to the heart.

Energy follows attention. When you are excessively
cerebral, energy feeds the head center. The same energy
that feeds the thinking center feeds the feeling center. Your
emotions and ego play out their reactions through the
thinking center, creating mental and physical stress that
minimize your ability to *feel* your feelings or *experience* the
experience. When you are in reaction to your experience,
dialogues and images take place in your thinking center.
When you live in your head center, the heart is starved.
Merging into experience happens through the medium of
feeling. When you enter the feeling center, separation
melts and you merge into a flood of energy.

Amrit Yoga provides powerful techniques that engage all of your attention into bodily sensation. This brings the attention and energy down from your thinking center to your feeling center. By engaging in an unbroken stream of attention on your bodily sensations, you increase the *flow* of energy into a *flood* of energy. You must stay totally aware of changes in sensation as your body shifts and assumes different positions.

Begin by being fully aware of every movement you make with your body.

As you practice postures (asanas), give your total undivided attention to all accompanying sensations that come and go. Remain unconditionally attentive and embrace whatever experience comes from performing the posture. Do not judge your performance or compare it with others. Drop all expectations. To be unconditionally present in the experience, you must enter into witness consciousness. Remain the witness, which makes no choices and has no expectations. The witness has no need to control or to improve. It has no fear or resistance to what is present. It removes the self-doubt, hesitation, self-judgment, fear or resistance that often shows up on the yoga mat. Call on the witness to observe. Allow

44

yourself to feel and experience whatever ⸍

the witness and fire the judge.

By embracing all bodily sensations, pleasure or pa⸍

comfort or discomfort, you experience the experience rather than reacting to it. All reactions come from internal conflict and disturbance. Witnessing your reactions rather than reacting to them helps you feel your feelings and let them go. Choiceless awareness will automatically enhance what is positive and diffuse what is negative. All the shifts that occur through the witness bring deeper unity. Shifts that are caused by the self-image (ego) bring more conflict. So enter the experience whole-heartedly and be fully present for whatever is before you.

It is most important to move slowly in and out of the postures.

Deliberately slow down every movement with meditative awareness. When you perform slow-motion movements with focused awareness of the breath, it is easier for your mind to tune in to bodily sensations. Moving slowly and very consciously, engage all your attention on the internal experience of what is happening. Observe not only your bodily sensations but also your mental reactions. Remain in the witness regardless of whatever arises as a disturbance from within or without.

This technique of tuning in to sensation naturally anchors the restless mind and gathers dissipated energy. In yoga, this is called *pratyahara*. Its purpose is to refocus fully again and again on the feeling center. The power of focused attention, concentration and consciousness aids you in making the shift from a body-centered practice to holistic integration of body, mind and spirit.

When the mind returns to where your body is,
when your mind does what your body is doing,
when your mind is totally focused on what
your body is feeling,
when your thoughts, feelings and actions
are moving as one,
you merge into the integrative experience of yoga.

Stay present for the second half of the posture.
Each time you finish a posture, there is a release of tension, as well as a flood of energy. As you focus your undivided attention on the sensations, the flow of energy is magnified. Allow yourself to enter into the celebration of deep release. The period that follows the actual holding of a posture is the other half of the posture. If you miss it, no matter how well you have performed, you have gone only half way. Your integrative process is most active in this interim period when you may think you have already finished your posture.

Awareness of the physical body is a means of establishing unity with the subtler bodies.
We perform many habitual activities with our body. We put food in our mouths, but we are not fully present to taste, smell and experience the texture of the food. We hear music, but we are not fully conscious in our listening, so we are not aware of the great variety of instruments, their intonations and diversity of sounds. We love others, but we have conditions and expectations that keep us from experiencing who they are. Conditions contaminate every experience and expression of love.

If you approach the practice of yoga with conditions, you will experience a reaction that comes from your expectation of what it should be like. It will be the experience of conflict between what you expect and what is present.

When you are unconditionally present and become aware of the food you are eating, the music you are listening to, or being in the company of your beloved, you become open, sensitive and receptive to subtleties that allow you to enjoy the experience. When you enjoy it, it is engaging and absorbing. When it is more engaging, it is also more fulfilling, satisfying and uplifting. Your heart center opens. You love what you do because it engages you fully. Then it becomes an experience of union of the body, mind, heart and spirit.

To reestablish the broken link between the physical, mental and emotional bodies, the practice of choiceless awareness is essential. Choiceless awareness allows us to be more present and more sensitive to our bodily sensations. If we are insensitive and unaware of our gross physical body, we cannot be sensitive to the subtlety of the mental and emotional bodies.

Focusing on bodily sensation while remaining the witness dissolves karmic blocks. This progressively increases your *sense-ability* to your physical body. Once you have established intimate contact with your body through increased sensitivity, you will have greater ability to use your body to let go of anger, blame, hatred and fear.

Yoga is about experiencing the sensation as it is, without trying to change it or modify it in any way.

Witness Consciousness

*The Doorway to Awakening your Dormant Powers
and Self-Discovery*

Witness consciousness (meditative awareness) is the core of Amrit Yoga. It is a way of disassociating from our self-image, an entity that obscures our true Self. Just as the clouds move away to reveal the light of the sun, when the mask of the self-image is removed, the Self shines through. Unmasking the Self is the process of Self-discovery. The witness creates the possibility of letting go of our identification with our preprogrammed self-image.

Both the self-image and the Self operate under the central unifying force of ego—the individual sense of "I am." When "I am" identifies with the self-image, it becomes a separative force. The self-image evolves from unresolved experiences of the past (karma). Out of these experiences arise fear and attachments, attractions and repulsions, likes and dislikes. The entire body of our personal history is an entity we call our personality, which comes from the Greek word 'persona' for mask. It is the masking by the phantom self that hides the real Self.

The self-image is comprised of our self-concepts, belief systems and personal biases that have been programmed into our unconscious by our parents, peers, teachers and society. The unconscious survives because we identify with our self-concepts and personal biases as "me." These personal biases manifest through our mental and emotional bodies. They are extensions of the self-image and they have a seductive hold over us. Meditative awareness is the most powerful tool you have to loosen the grip of identification of the self-image as "me."

The conflict perpetrated by the self-image prevents you from discovering who you truly are.

To be released from this unconsciousness that separates you from the true Self, you must step back from the distortions and filters imposed by the self-image. The most direct way to accomplish this is through witness consciousness. The witness creates an opening for you to let go of past conditioning and everything that is holding you back.

Meditative awareness creates an opening for you to move out of personal biases and prejudices and into impersonal reality.

When you are unbiased, clear and objective, you have the facility to solve problems, resolve conflicts within yourself and in every interaction of life. Personal biases are the source of all problems; impersonal reality is the source of all solutions.

Yoga is a journey from personal perception to impersonal clarity and objectivity, from individual to universal. The subjective self-image is in a perpetual quarrel with universal reality. As you practice meditation in motion, you will experience the shift from personal projections to impersonal reality. The more personal addictions and fears you have, the greater the conflict with reality. As you grow in the witness, your biases grow weaker and your ability to tolerate reality grows stronger.

The witness is non-judgmental self-observation.

Your unconscious identification with your personality as yourself feeds the self-image. You also reinforce the self-image by trying to get rid of it. The moment you become the witness of your own thoughts, emotional reactions and personal likes and dislikes, you discontinue feeding the self-image. Instead of fighting your self-image, starve it by using witness consciousness. As the witness starves the self-image, the Higher Self begins to reveal itself. Yoga is a process of unmasking the Self.

The self-image produces mental and emotional static.

Ongoing mental and emotional static accompanies you wherever you go and whatever you do. When you are unaware, this internal static is always present, whether you are driving your car, cooking food, cleaning house or performing yoga postures. This chronic disturbance and conflict is what keeps you from being fully and totally present. It depletes your life energy, draining you of vitality, creativity and efficiency.

The presence of stress prevents you from harmony of body, mind, heart and spirit. Meditative awareness helps quiet the internal static. This automatically turns on the music of the soul.

In Amrit Yoga, the central focus is on eliminating the internal conflict that diminishes the power of yoga. It helps you develop integrative awareness along with the practice of postures. Being in the state of witness consciousness during your practice prevents the mind from engaging in internal conflicts. Mental dialogues create conflict and instantly translate into tensions in the body. Witness consciousness makes you aware of the stress-producing mental and emotional dialogues and helps you breathe, relax and let them go.

Yoga is a journey of Self-discovery.
Awareness helps you withdraw attention from external and internal disturbances (pratyahara) to focus undivided attention on bodily sensations (dharana). Witnessing and embracing both pleasure and pain, likes and dislikes through meditation (dhyana) prevent you from reacting to disturbances. In this state, you create the possibility for self-observation and self-discovery. Centering your focus on bodily sensation and breath is the most powerful device you have to anchor scattered attention. It also lays the groundwork for the integrative process. As you practice awareness along with postures, you will begin to move through deeper layers of tensions. These "blocks" of tension manifest as pain in the body and fear in the mind. The witness prevents you from reacting to pain and fear, and creates an opening to cross the boundaries of the body-mind.

This state of choiceless awareness does not mean you have eliminated options. On the contrary, it means you have eliminated limitations set by your belief systems and preprogrammed self-concepts that tell you what you can and cannot do. Then you are no longer victimized by self-destructive reactions to the past.

Integration

Embracing the Opposites: Moving from Duality to Polarity to Unity

As explained in the yoga scriptures, the purpose of Hatha Yoga is to bring about the balance and unification of "Ha" (the sun breath) and "Tha" (the moon breath). The breaths that flow through the sun and the moon represent the two wings of the soul. Breath is the medium through which the soul manifests in the body. All life-giving processes are carried out by the involuntary function of the polarity of "breathing in" and "breathing out."

Through the continuous, dedicated practice of Hatha Yoga, the polarized currents of sun and moon— pingala and ida—unite and begin to flow through the *shushumna*, which represents the unification of the individual soul, *jivatman* and the supreme soul, *paramatman*. This is the ultimate experience of the eight-limbed *Ashtanga Yoga*. It represents the total unification of the conflicting dualities of opposing forces. This integration is called Hatha Yoga.

Life begins with the first breath *in* and ends with the last breath *out*. In between, life is sustained by the uninterrupted flow of breath, whether you are awake or asleep, conscious or unconscious. When the breath leaves, so too does the soul. This is why, in yoga, both the breath *and* the soul are called prana. The biological prana that initiates life through breath is the direct extension of Prana, the Soul. When the integrated state of the soul manifests as life-giving breath, it is revealed through the polarity of "Ha" and "Tha," Sun and Moon, Pingala and Ida. This is when the state of unity manifests through the interactions of polarity throughout the body.

When the balance between pingala and ida is reestablished through the consistent practice of yoga, the middle channel of shushumna becomes active. You move out of the ego-centered, disturbing interaction among the physical, mental and emotional bodies that appear in the field of duality. The ultimate obstruction in the process of unification of polarity is identification with the self-image, which operates through the personality and wears the mask of the false self. This separation from the source of the Self is the act of the ego. When the separative identity of the ego is transformed, all imbalances of the interaction of the sun and moon that cause stress, fatigue, fear and mental restlessness, are removed. When the separation of the individual soul from the cosmic soul is unified, it is called *Samadhi*.

The ultimate purpose of yoga practice is to induce an integrative process, balancing the opposing polarities of the sun breath and the moon breath, the male and female principle. It is not meant to be a muscle-building or cardiovascular exercise such as calisthenics. Yoga postures performed without the integrative, feminine principle minimize the powerful impact of yoga. When we are engaged in one-sided aggressive male action without its balancing female counterpart, it becomes more like exercise, which may be useful, but it is not yoga.

Male energy, Purusha, is active. Female energy, Prakriti, is receptive. It is the combined power of *"making it happen"* and *"letting it happen"* that creates the experience of union—of Shiva and Shakti. To focus solely on the body, without harnessing the forces that actively work through the conflicting duality of attractions and repulsions, addiction and fears, is to consciously choose one polarized opposite over the other, producing imbalance *within* the body and mind in the form of physical tension, mental irritation and emotional disturbance, as well as the interaction *between* the body and mind. The intention of this practice is to return to the Source. The Source we call union, oneness, God, *Paramatman*, the Supreme Soul.

Expansion and contraction, tension and relaxation, activity and receptivity are continuously in dynamic interaction of the balancing process. When the ego-mind, however, manifests its addictions and fears, attractions and repulsions, and works excessively through one side of the polarity of breath, it disturbs the harmonious polarity of sun and moon/yin and yang energy. This creates imbalance experienced as emotional conflict, mental irritation and physical stress, which is at the core of all human suffering and sickness. The choice between one pole and the other, for or against either side, alters *impersonal complementary polarity* into a *personal experience of conflicting duality*.

The polarity principle actively carries out all life-giving processes. These processes are guided in our body by the universal intelligence of prana through the complementary interaction of tension and relaxation in the muscles, expansion and contraction of the heart, lungs, arteries and veins, inspiration and expiration of breath, and nurturance through assimilation and elimination. Interference with these self-sustaining processes manifested through ego-imbalances results in changes in your physical, emotional and mental health.

The quality of life you experience is determined by the degree of balance or imbalance present in the breath patterns. These breath patterns are strongly affected by the *condition* of the body and mind. When the unconscious forces of the ego-mind identify with the self-image, it disengages from the *complementary polarity* and decides to resolve life's problems by choosing life and fearing death, addiction to pleasure and fear of pain, becoming so attached to success that we are afraid of failure. Fear forces us to operate from extremes, of one side or the other, seeking relief and disturbing the complementary interaction of polarity. All of these opposites cause us to excessively operate from one side of polarity and create physical, mental and emotional disturbances that reflect as imbalances. The two main channels of polarity feed the entire chakra system, which, if imbalanced, disturbs the nerves that activate the functions of the organs for optimal performance.

What we experience in life depends upon whether our body, mind and breath are managed through the channel of the dualistic ego-mind or integrative awareness.

Through the practice of Amrit Yoga, we initiate the complementary dynamic interaction of polarity that helps us to move beyond conflicting duality into the state of unity.

Moving from Polarity to Unity in Amrit Yoga:
> – *creates a broad range of experience—from deep silence to dynamic activity.*
> – *is an integrated experience—a paradoxical union of dynamic motion and meditative absorption.*
> – *alternates between dynamic animated postures and deeply absorbing, engaging silence.*

The impact of deliberate dynamic postures is echoed in the deeply absorbing silence and the relaxation that follows. The depth you enter during the dynamic posture is automatically reversed into deep relaxation. Relaxation is a rebound action—the direct response to deliberately assumed depth of the asana.

The alternating impact of internal and external, tension and relaxation, active and passive, meditation and motion, increases your ability to enter progressively deeper levels in the active posture and non-active (passive) meditation.

The active, conscious integration of action and non-action enhances and empowers the other. The opposites act as a unit, becoming a powerful pair where opposites co-create a complementary experience of union. This is union—this is yoga.

The depth of absorption and relaxation you attain depends directly upon the depth you enter during the dynamic part of the asana. During the practice of Amrit Yoga, you alternate between the external form (asana) and the internal state of formless being. It is the marriage of male and female, conscious activity and conscious receptivity.

The specific sequence of postures not only takes you to the deepest levels of relaxation, but also helps you to transform stressful shadow energies into love and light in the Third Eye. The alternating rhythm of shifting from form to formless being, from the active body to the silent soul is the experience of yoga, of embodying the spirit.

Form comes from doing; formlessness emerges from being. The purpose of doing is *being* what you are *doing*—where the dancer disappears into the dance, where the performer merges into the performance. In this state of integration, all healing miracles occur spontaneously. Where I am not, God is. When "I" as the achiever, performer and doer disappears, "I" become the open channel for God to come through and perform miracles.

In Amrit Yoga, asanas are practiced deliberately, not aggressively or forcefully. Aggressiveness is distortion of the pure male energy. Willful action performed consciously and deliberately is *Purusha*, making it happen. It is practiced in combination with *Prakriti*, letting it happen, which is also called surrender.

This combination of making it happen and letting it happen, will and surrender, is the play of male and female, doing and being, form and formlessness, Shiva and Shakti.

Making it happen and letting it happen empower you to take flight into the vastness of the limitless sky of your consciousness. Engaging in aggressive male energy, while ignoring the receptive female energy is like a bird trying to fly by flapping just one wing. As the bird's two wings fulfill the single function of flying, your practice of yoga soars when you learn to integrate the complementary forces of doing and being, meditation and motion.

Amrit Yoga engages the wings of your body and of your being, the physical form and the formless being. Using both your wings empowers you to transcend the limits of your body and mind to explore and experience the non-physical, non-mental domain of the spirit that you are.

Self-Inquiry

I invite you to explore unknown challenges and to realize hidden potentials. The practice of Amrit Yoga provides you with the unlimited potential to experience deeper physical, mental and emotional releases, as well as enhanced awareness. If you have asked yourself any of the following questions, Amrit Yoga will provide the answers, not just intellectually, but experientially as well.

1. *How do I perform postures to maximize the release of the mental and emotional tensions I hold in my body?*

2. *During my practice of yoga, my mind is always wandering. It consistently slips away and I find myself thinking of anything but what I am doing. How can I focus my attention on and off the yoga mat?*

3. *My body is stiff. What can I do to overcome the stiffness? Is it possible for someone like me to practice yoga and get the full benefits of yoga?*

4. *I am afraid of hurting and pulling my muscles during the practice. This fear keeps me from enjoying and going deeper into the experience of yoga. How can I prevent injury and release the fear of injury?*

5. *I need healing. I am recuperating from an illness and my body is aging. Can I still practice yoga?*

6. *How can I maximize the healing and relaxing therapeutic effects of yoga?*

7. *I have practiced the Hatha Yoga asana stage fairly well. How can I learn to integrate the next stages of Ashtanga Yoga: pratyahara (withdrawal of outgoing attention), dharana (concentration), and dhyana (meditation) in my practice?*

8. I have been doing yoga regularly but my practice is becoming mechanical and often uninteresting. How can I expand the scope and deepen my practice to make it a more rewarding, enjoyable and engaging experience?

9. What relevance does yoga practice and philosophy have to key personal issues, such as relationships, family, work, decision-making and realization of my potential?

The Three Stages of Amrit Yoga

Stage I *Willful Practice*

The main focus in the first stage is to learn to perform the postures correctly but without force. In Amrit Yoga, willful practice means you are deliberately attempting to work through your personal fears and physical inhibitions. The willful approach is neither aggressive nor forceful. Willful practice does not violate or override the wisdom of the body. Instead it works with the body consciously and deliberately.

Enter each posture with awareness and respect for the body. Focusing on proper form and alignment does not mean forcing yourself to achieve perfection of the final form. Instead remain focused on performing the posture to the best of your ability. It is correct form, not the perfection of the posture that provides the maximum benefits.

- *Follow precision, alignment and attention to the details.*
- *Make your movements slow, focused and intentional to help you go through some areas of your body that you might otherwise avoid.*
- *Pay attention to what your body can and cannot do, rather than judge or compare your performance with others.*
- *Do everything possible to keep your attention inwardly focused.*

As you approach the practice, accept the limitations in your body. Your journey begins from where you are. It cannot begin from where you are not. So drop internal resistance when you discover your physical limitations. Breathe, relax and let go of stress and holding as you encounter the inhibitions in your body.

Self-acceptance will prevent you from judging yourself or comparing yourself with others. You will become more relaxed and remain more attentive and focused on what is happening within you. This form of self-acceptance will allow you to let go of the fears, insecurities and resistance that often undermine your ability to work more effectively with yourself.

Stage II *Will and Surrender*

After you have learned to perform the postures well, deepen your internal focus, allowing your movements to be slow and deliberate. The slowness will allow you to become more aware, relaxed and internally focused in your practice.

Every time you complete a posture, pay close attention to your bodily sensations. As your attention deepens, you will enter the flood of energy that is released during the posture. The period that follows the actual performance of a posture is the other half of the posture. The posture of integrative consciousness extends beyond the completion of the physical posture. If you miss it, no matter how well you have performed, you have gone only half way. Your integrative process is most active in this interim period when you may think you have already finished your posture.

Deepening your internal awareness helps you to recognize subtler sources of tension and to release them. Awareness keeps you more focused, attentive and aware of bodily sensations. It plays an important role in connecting the co-creative power of the body-mind. In the second stage, you continue to slow down your movements and begin to withdraw your attention from disturbances that arise from within and without. The more attentive and aware you are, the more you can remain inwardly focused and the greater the impact on your practice. When the mental and emotional disturbances take over your attention and create internal conflict, gently redirect your undivided attention back to internal bodily sensations.

Integration continues regardless of where you are—while actively engaged in the performance of the posture, holding the posture, in transition, resting in between or in a complementary posture. When you are engaged in the posture of integrative consciousness, you are in a spiritual posture that transcends your physical posture. When you become established in the "posture of consciousness," there is no conclusion to the posture.

In the will and surrender stage, you also consciously prolong the holding of postures. During the prolonged holding, learn how to cross the fear boundaries that show up when you encounter pain in your body. When you come out of a prolonged holding, it is very important to sit up straight, relax and continue to focus on internal bodily sensations. When you pay close attention to the bodily sensations, it instantly releases the flood of energy. Attention automatically increases and intensifies the flow of prana. Let your whole body be bathed in the healing river of prana. Dive deeper into the internal energy experience and remain there until you melt, merge and disappear.

As you learn to withdraw your attention from external and internal disturbances (pratyahara), refocus it on the bodily sensations that are present (dharana) and use meditative awareness (dhyana) to eliminate any mental or emotional reactions that arise during the holding of the posture. This enables you to penetrate deeper layers of stress and emotional traumas of the past. The deeper you go, the more energy released.

When you prolong the holding of the postures you invariably uncover unresolved hurtful experiences and fears that are built into your muscle memory. When old memories surface, the usual reaction is to resist, fight or avoid the experience. The fight or flight reflex is an unconscious instinctive reaction. When that happens, breathe, relax and let go of the tension. Use meditative awareness to keep from "reacting to your reactions." The witness will bring your attention from your thinking center to your feeling center. At all times, keep your undivided attention on bodily sensations. Whether you are in the posture, in transition or in relaxation, maintain your unbroken stream of attention on bodily sensations. Constant inward focus re-establishes the body-mind connection.

Each time you prolong the holding, there is a build-up of energy. So when you release the posture, your body will naturally guide you into a complementary posture. This guidance comes directly from the wisdom of your prana-body. Allow yourself to surrender to the impulses and guidance that arise from your body. Assume different positions as directed by the wisdom emerging directly from your body.

Stage III *Surrender*

To enter the stage of surrender, you must understand the relationship that exists between your physical body, prana body and mental body. In this stage, you shift from practicing willful postures to surrendering your movements to the wisdom of your body.

The force that produces involuntary life-giving bodily functions independent of your mind is called the wisdom of prana—the wisdom of the body. What is called involuntary function in physiology is recognized as the wisdom of the prana-body in yoga. Voluntary functions of the body are directly under the control of our will or mind. It is the energy of prana that carries out both voluntary and involuntary functions in our body.

When there are mental or emotional disturbances, the prana that carries out involuntary functions is also disturbed because prana follows mental commands. Prana mimics the mind. When we are caught in our unconscious emotional reactions, prana automatically becomes engaged in unconscious emotional reactions. We use up our life energy in self-destructive ways, depriving the mechanism of involuntary functions to carry out internal homeostatic and healing processes.

When prana works directly under the control of the mind, it performs voluntary functions of the body. When the distractions in the mind are removed, prana is automatically released to carry out internal healing functions at an accelerated rate. In this stage you surrender your will to the inner wisdom of your body. This greatly magnifies the rejuvenating and evolutionary impact of prana.

In Stage III you set aside rules and restrictions of the willful practice. You surrender and let go of everything that you have learned about postures, techniques from books or any other source. All of your movements are guided by the higher intelligence of prana from within. During the practice of the earlier two stages, you will have already released many blockages from your physical, mental and emotional bodies. This prepares you to move into surrender more easily. Thus when you allow your postures and movements to emerge from within, unedited by your mind, the wisdom of the body automatically choreographs and tailors the positions, the sequence, and the holding time to precisely suit your body's own needs. Such moments that originate directly from beyond the mind are spontaneous, effortless and deeply engaging. When we surrender our will to the wisdom of the body and allow its impulses to guide our movements—it is meditation in motion.

Preparation for Entering the Sacred Practice of Yoga

Begin your practice with a few deep breaths. Sit up straight. Relax your body. Bring your attention to this present moment. Feel calm and relaxed. Now slowly take a deep breath. Gradually exhale in the same slow and steady flow. Repeat this a few times. Let there be sound of the ocean (ujjayi) breath. As you breathe, listen to the unbroken sound of the breath going in and going out. Let this breathing calm your mind and relax your body. Now breathe normally and sit still. Read this prayer and attune yourself fully. Throughout the entire session your practice is geared toward this intention, which captures the spirit of yoga:

I open my heart to explore the divinity that is inherent within my being and my body. I respect and honor my body as the temple of the divine. I am not just this body but the embodied spirit itself.

When I step into yoga, I step into sacred territory. I move with great reverence towards my body. I take this sacred moment as an opportunity to transform the blockages and limitations in my physical, mental and emo-

tional bodies that keep me from realizing the divine poten-
tial inborn within me.

During this entire practice, I make a firm commitment
to apply myself one hundred percent in each posture, en-
gaging my full attention and choiceless awareness to fully
surrender to the experience of the moment, the sacred union
of body, mind, and spirit.

Let this intention be fully in your heart as you move
in this practice.

Om shanti, shanti, shanti. Peace, peace, peace.

Guided Sample for the Posture of Consciousness
(apply to all postures in general)

**Prepare yourself for the Standing Forward
Bend.** Move slowly and consciously so that you capture
every sensation that moves through your body. Stay relaxed. Bring your total attention to your body. Breathe
smoothly and deeply. Move with great awareness, no-
ticing every sensation that accompanies your movement. Your attention must be fully engaged by all the
sensations that emerge from changing positions. As you
hold the posture, focus your attention on the maximum

stretch that is felt in this posture, and where you feel it in your body. If you feel discomfort, relax. Take a deep breath, so that you may relax fully and move beyond any blocks you may encounter.

Now prepare for the Triangle Pose. As you move into this posture, pay attention to all the details of your bodily movement and its impact on your body. Honor your own body's limits, but at the same time, know how to consciously step out of the boundaries that your fear has created. Go a little further without being aggressive. When you reach the first urge to come out of the posture, relax even more. See if you can go beyond that first limit and consciously extend your holding time. As you hold the posture, move deeper into the stretch. Where you feel the maximum discomfort, relax, breathe deeply. (There is a tendency to hold the breath when you feel strained. At that time, relax and breathe deeply. Watch how breathing deeply helps you to let go of the defensive tension that keeps you from prolonging your holding or breaking through the tension.) Gradually release the posture, and in a slow steady motion, anchor your attention in the unbroken stream of changing sensations.

Come down into a seated position for the Child Pose. Continue to move slowly and steadily. Maintain choiceless awareness. Breathe deeply. Stay calm and relaxed, remaining fully attentive and engaged in the bodily experiences of pleasure and pain, comfort and discomfort. Remain fully in the sensations without labeling them.

Next move into the Cobra Posture. Let every one of your transition movements be very, very relaxed, like a meditative flow. Your attention remains inwardly focused throughout the transition. Let your movements be non-aggressive, conscious, and with intention to move beyond your habitual limits. Use the breath to remove energy blocks trapped in your unconscious, reactive patterns. With deliberate movements, work through the bodily limits imposed by your fear or self-concepts, consciously breaking through old habits. Go deeper, deliberately and consciously, not forcefully. Relax into the posture.

With meditative awareness, release the posture, paying attention to the delightful sensation that comes after holding. Notice the equal degree of relaxation that follows. Sit up straight, relaxed, upright. The energy blocks that were released are now integrated into your body. Enjoy the feeling of experiencing a whole new relationship between your body and your mind, a new friendship. Feel the joy of synchronicity of your body, mind and spirit that is so integral to your practice. Move through the remainder of your practice with the same meditative awareness.

Gradually come out of your final posture and sit quietly for a few moments. Always allow some time after the completion of the posture for integration.

Focus on these principles each time you practice. Let yourself rejoice in what is present at any given time. Every time your attention wanders, reenter your body through the sensations that are always present in your body. If the sensations are rewarding and joyous, you feel that. If they are painful or uncomfortable, you relax into it. You're not fighting it. You're not trying to get rid of it, but just staying with it. Relax, and let go of any holding.

Acknowledge what a tremendous difference you have made in your life as you give your body and mind a new relationship, a new integration by being in the witness consciousness. Realize that this integration of the body, mind and spirit is making you whole, bringing you to a new level of awareness in your life. Return to the stillness within. Know that the power to resolve all the problems of life is within you.

Guidelines for Practicing Amrit Yoga

After you have learned to perform yoga postures correctly, integrate the following principles to increase the
depth and expand the scope of your practice:

1. Perform your yoga practice in the spirit of sacred
sadhana (spiritual practice).

2. Steadily hold your internal focus on the con-
stantly shifting sensations and changing positions. This
keeps your attention from wandering. Combining meditative choiceless awareness with inwardly focused attention creates the integrated experience of body, mind
and spirit.

3. Keep your unbroken stream of attention totally
focused on the sensations in the area of the body that
are most activated during the holding, after the release
of the posture, during transition from one posture to another, and during rest periods.

4. Each time you finish holding a yoga posture, remain totally absorbed and internally focused, bathing

in the flood of energy that is released. Participate in the celebration of the deep ecstasy of union that follows. The release from the posture is the second half of the posture. The integration process, the posture of consciousness, continues beyond the completion of the active part of the posture.

5. The completion of the posture is the most active part. Paying more attention to sensations increases the flood of energy into a river of energy. Bathing your body in the sacred river of prana purifies and heals your body.

6. During the passive part of a posture (the transition time or rest time), remain fully attentive to the energy release from the holding. Consciously allow the released energy (Shakti) from the bondage of the unconscious shadow self to rise and merge into the light of consciousness of the Third Eye (Shiva Netra). This is the most important part of releasing Shakti from the bondage of your shadow self and delivering her to Shiva. Each time you do this, the passage from Shakti to Shiva through *shashumna nadi* (located along the spine) is progressively cleared. A posture performed with integrative yoga consciousness is the dance of Shiva and Shakti.

7. Focus your total attention on bodily sensation. Remain in choiceless witness, embracing all the bodily sensations that come and go. Remove labels of pleasure or pain, success or failure, right or wrong. Enter with the beginner's mind and experience the pure sensation. In the absence of labeling, judging, analyzing or doubting, Shakti has complete freedom to dance in step with consciousness. The dance of Shiva and Shakti will lead to deeper stillness and tranquility in the midst of movement.

8. Explore, encounter and disperse the deeper and subtler blocks by focusing your attention and integrative awareness on your bodily sensations. Shakti feeds the area of attention, greatly magnifying the benefits and the impact of the posture.

9. When you are in prolonged holding of the posture, explore surrounding areas by using improvised movements. This expands the opportunity to address the areas of the body that you might have ignored.

10. Let integrative yoga consciousness be a constant companion to move your body, mind and spirit as one unit. Honor your body and prepare it as a sacred temple to invoke the presence of the divine spirit.

11. When your body, mind and spirit move as one, you enter a sacred space. You have entered the yoga posture of integration.

12. The body is the gross mind. The mind is the subtle body. Allow your body, mind and integrative spirit to be in co-creation. Co-creation allows you to explore the depth of the posture, increasing its effectiveness manyfold.

13. The true meaning of yoga is revealed in the direct experience of yoga and is actualized only when you experience internal integration. Through the medium of non-participative witness of changing sensations of pleasure and pain, comfort and discomfort, you will be able to let go of your reactions to fear and pain.

14. In the absence of mental and emotional disturbance, your awareness and attention penetrate into deeper and subtler layers of tensions, dissolving and releasing a flood of prana that performs miracles of healing.

Inspirational Quotes to Explore, Expand & Experience the Deeper Meaning of Yoga

"There is a source of spiritual power always present within you. To reclaim this source of higher consciousness, you must first recognize this most empowering truth—I am the creator of my present and future, regardless of what happened in the past. Because of this truth, there is the possibility for every individual to realize and experience the mysterious liberating power of grace and beauty of his or her soul"

"Amrit Yoga uses the body as an entry point to explore, experience and release psychosomatic blocks that prevent you from tapping into the source of infinite potential within. It is easily accessible for beginners, advanced students and yoga teachers who want to add new depth to their practice and teaching."

"While honoring all yoga traditions, Amrit Yoga expands the popular concept of yoga as a physical discipline into bio-spiritual dimensions. It creates new possibilities for widening the range of healing modalities and self-discovery. The concepts are adaptable to various levels of healing and therapeutic applications, as well as for spiritual growth."

"This approach to yoga teaches you not only how to face challenges on the yoga mat, but also how to use challenges you encounter in life—painful transition periods, relationships and crises—as an opening for personal transformation."

"The powers of ego are separative and self-destructive. When you enter the experience of unity—yoga—the body and mind are infused and empowered to manifest the soul."

"When you are integrated, total and undivided, you tap into the unlimited source of potential within you. The yoga of integrative consciousness greatly magnifies the power of your yoga practice."

"In search of the divine we go everywhere. We go to places of pilgrimage, visit temples, follow many paths and disciplines—and ignore our bodies. Your body is the most sacred place of pilgrimage you'll ever come to. It is the dwelling place of the divine spirit; it is the temple of God. Go within and experience the glory of God within you."

"What holds you back in the practice of yoga—or any spiritual practice—is not your weaknesses, but the fear that either fights or avoids your fear. Fear that fights is worse than the weakness it fights. When you fight your weakness, you feed it."

"The practice of yoga leads to an experience of unity. When you embrace opposites fully and totally, it manifests into a paradoxical experience. Paradox is the ultimate dimension of sacred union—yoga—where opposites are no longer in conflict, where duality manifests as oneness, where meditation and movement, emptiness and fullness, activity and inactivity, effort and effortlessness, become one."

About Yogi Amrit Desai

Yogi Amrit Desai, also known as Gurudev, is an internationally renowned yoga master, seminar leader and author in the field of yoga and holistic living. In 1970, Yogi Desai had a Kundalini awakening experience by the grace of his Siddha Guru, H.H. Swami Kripalvanandji, which permanently changed his life and shattered the model of yoga he had been practicing and teaching.

Out of this experience, he developed a spiritual dimension to the practice of Hatha Yoga, a methodology that altered the popular notion of yoga as a physical discipline. He called it Meditation in Motion and named this new approach Kripalu Yoga in honor of his guru.

The yoga society he founded in the early 1960s grew into a yoga ashram, which became the Kripalu Center for Yoga and Health. Kripalu became one of the largest yoga centers of its kind in America. Today thousands of certified yoga teachers around the world teach the methodology he developed. He continues to teach and develop his innovative approach in the form of Amrit Yoga.

He has been repeatedly recognized and honored in India and abroad for carrying the true and authentic voice of yoga to the world. Some of his numerous awards and titles include: Doctor of Yoga by H. H. Jagatguru Shankaracharaya, Jagadacharaya (Universal Teacher) by the World Religious Parliament in New Delhi, and the rare Vishwa Yoga Ratna awarded by the President of India. He was also nominated for the highest honor of India, Padma Vibhushan, by former Prime Minster Chandra Shekhar.

For more than four decades, the impact of his teachings has reached hundreds of thousands of people around the world. Being in the presence of Yogi Desai is a unique opportunity to learn directly from a true master of yoga. Thousands have experienced the awesome power of shakti embodied by Yogi Desai. It radiates through his presence, his discourses, mantra chanting, guided meditations and his demonstration of meditation in motion. Its powerful synergetic impact is transmitted to all those who are receptive and open.

Glossary

Amrita–from Hindu mythology, a nectar of life. In Sanskrit, the prefix "a" means "not," the root "mrta" means "dead." Amrita is the drink of immortality. Immortality is the ultimate stage that yogis aspire to. Amrita is the divine elixir that heals all human suffering caused by separative consciousness.

Acceptance–ceasing resistance, absence of reaction to what is present in reality.

Asanas–yoga postures.

Ashtanga–the eight-limbed yoga system as explained in the *Yoga Sutras* codified by Patanjali in the 2nd century BCE.

Atman–soul, Higher Self, eternal Source.

Awareness–represents the meditative perception of reality without personal bias.

Bhakti Yoga–The yoga of love, devotion and selfless service.

Chakras–The seven centers (wheels) of energy/consciousness located in the subtle body, where we receive, transmit, and process life energies (see prana). The chakras are astral centers, corresponding to the nerve plexuses in the spine. Each chakra has specific characteristics corresponding to a particular state of consciousness.

Choiceless awareness (see witness consciousness)

Darshan–an audience with a spiritual master or a saint.

Direct experience–experiencing directly without the interference or distortion from preprogrammed personal biases; experience beyond the rational mind with beginner's mind, which is received at a cellular level.

Duality–when natural polarity is altered by personal preferences for or against what is present, it becomes duality. Through this personal preference, the complementary polarity in nature becomes conflicting duality for those who attempt to separate one pole from the other, which is experienced as internal conflict. (See polarity.)

Dharna–concentration, one of the limbs of Ashtanga Yoga. Part of the mental discipline of Raja Yoga.

Dhyana–meditation; one of the limbs of Ashtanga Yoga. It is the window for the entrance to the spiritual dimension of the discipline of Ashtanga Yoga.

Ecstasy–derived from the Greek, "to stand outside of oneself." In yoga, it is the ultimate orgasmic experience of the union of Shiva and Shakti, known as Samadhi. It is the experience of union with the Self that has completely liberated from the limitations of the self-image.

Experiential (see direct experience)

Hatha Yoga–represents a physical component of the mental and spiritual discipline of Raja Yoga. Together, they form Patanjali's classical system of eight-limbed Ashtanga Yoga.

Integration–the process of bringing together the physical, mental, emotional and spiritual bodies to function and act in complete balance and harmony as a unit. Integration—union—is the basic purpose for the practice of yoga.

Karma–the law of cause and effect: every action has an opposite and equal reaction. (As you sow, so shall you reap.) Karma is the experience of unresolved incomplete experiences of the past, returning again and again in the present, giving us new opportunities to encounter it consciously and resolve it. The action we perform is called karma and the reaction to the action that we experience is also the result of karma.

Kriyas–spontaneous physical manifestations directly activated by awakened Kundalini in the form of Hatha Yoga postures, pranayamas, locks, mudras, and cleansing kriyas, leading toward the highest state of Samadhi.

Kundalini–the primordial cosmic energy that lies coiled at the base of the spine. When awakened, Kundalini begins to move upward, penetrating the chakras and initiating various yogic kriyas, which bring about total purification, rejuvenation and transformation of the entire being, leading to the ultimate state of Samadhi, the state of immortality.

Mantra–powerful sound vibrations which, when chanted continuously, have a calming and purifying effect on the nervous system, mind and heart; sacred sounds of power which release potent spiritual energies within the chanter.

Meditation–objective impersonal observation of whatever becomes the object of our awareness; the development of non-judgmental witness which allows us to embrace opposites unconditionally and takes us from the field of duality to the sacred state of unity and oneness.

Meditative Awareness (see witness consciousness)

Mudras–various hand gestures and physical positions prompted spontaneously by the awakened Kundalini that create internal movement of the energy to mobilize and direct the energies to break through blockages in the physical, mental and emotional bodies.

Om–the primordial sound, which represents unity; the essence of all mantras.

Patanjali–often called the Father of Yoga; first to formally record yogic practices as the eight limbs of yoga in the 2nd century BCE.

Polarity–in nature, polarity is complementary and operates in harmony as a unit (one pole cannot exist without the other); it exists in the form of attraction and repulsion, birth and death, expansion and contraction. (See duality)

Prana–the primal intelligent energy that regulates the macrocosm of the entire universe as well as the universe in microcosm-the human body; represents the soul as well as the vital breath.

Pranayama–breathing techniques that regulate, control and restrain the breath; one of the disciplines of yoga that extends the power of prana.

Pratyahara–Retrieving outgoing attention, one of the eight limbs of Ashtanga Yoga.

Raja Yoga–the mental discipline of yoga.

Sadhana–all spiritual practices.

Samadhi–the eighth limb of Ashtanga Yoga; the final experience of the ultimate union of the individual soul with the cosmic soul.

Satsang–in the company of truth (literal): spiritual gathering.

Self–soul that denotes both Supreme soul as well as individual soul; according to Vedanta, ancient scriptures, both are identical.

Self-Discovery–the process of disassociation from identification with our self-image as our Self; uncovering all the layers that simultaneously reveals the Self that is hidden behind the mask of the self-image.

Sensation (bodily)–ability to feel what is present without the preprogrammed preference of being for or against the experience; it is a felt-sense experience.

Separative Ego–The self-image, which is born of our self-concepts. When we identify with our self-image as our true self, we are separated from ourselves, from others, and from our Higher Self.

Seva–selfless service; fosters an attitude of selflessness and spiritual awareness.

Shanti–Peace.

Shakti–the female force or energy. It is the divine cosmic energy, which projects, maintains and dissolves the universe; portrayed as the universal mother.

Shiva–consciousness; also a name for the all-pervasive supreme reality; one or the Hindu trinity, representing the process of transformation.

Shushumna–subtle nerve channel within the spinal column, extending from the base of the spine to the brain through which awakened Kundalini rises; it is the pathway to the ultimate experience of union—yoga.

Surrender–letting go of the ego (self), not of the Self; willingness to be open and to wholeheartedly embrace all experiences without judgment. Surrender is letting go of all that holds us back from being one with our divine Self.

Third Eye–sacred spot between the eyebrows where integration occurs; its location is the sixth chakra.

Yamas & **Niyamas**–ethical guidelines that help protect and prevent distractions and disturbances that come from within and from without.

Yoga–union of the individual soul with the cosmic soul; the ecstatic experience of the union of Shiva and Shakti; the state of oneness with the Higher Self.

Yoga Nidra–a conscious connection with your subconscious where you enter the alpha state; in this state the mystical powers of the third eye are released, actualizing the healing power of affirmations, visualizations and prayers.

Witness Consciousness–(non-participative choiceless awareness or meditative awareness)—the non-judgmental, impersonal observer.

Yogi Desai's audio and videotapes on guided yoga, meditation, chanting and relaxation, and his lectures on a variety of topics are available. He also gives seminars on yoga,
health and healing, personal growth and transformation.

The Amrit Yoga Asana Sequence is a
specific set of 26 postures designed to create awareness and integration of body,
mind, heart and spirit—the posture of
consciousness™. You can learn the sequence from guided instruction through
our CD collection and charts, or through
an Amrit Yoga-certified teacher. Visit
www.amrityoga.org to learn more about
teachers in your area or our Amrit Yoga
Teacher Training programs, Level I, II,
and Master's degree certification through
the Hindu University of America.

For information on:

Seminars...
Amrit Yoga Institute
PO Box 5340
Salt Springs, FL 32134
email: info@amrityoga.org
phone: (352) 685-3001
www.amrityoga.org

Products...
Amrit Kala
email: info@amritkala.com
phone: (352) 685-2855
www.amritkala.com

Editor: Lila Ivey   Photographers: Malay Desai, Peter Goldberg

3rd Printing.